A Giraffe Book

The Life of Jesus

Stories from the New Testament
retold by Margaret Ralph

Illustrated by Gordon King

Scripture Union/Purnell

News for Mary

Mary sang softly as she helped her mother in the house. Joseph had asked her to marry him, and soon she was going to be his wife. This made her very happy, for she loved Joseph.

As she was working, Mary looked round and saw someone standing in the doorway. There was light all around him. Mary hid her face in her hands, for she saw that it was an angel.

'Don't be afraid, Mary,' he said. 'God has sent me to you. You will have a baby boy and you must call him Jesus. He will be your child, but he will also be the Son of God.'

'How can this be?' asked Mary.

'God can do everything,' the angel said. 'God will be with you.'

'I will do whatever God asks,' said Mary. 'Let it be just as he says.'

Then the angel left Mary.

Luke 1. 26–38

The baby in the stable

'Look, Mary, there is Bethlehem,'
said Joseph.

Mary looked up and saw the little
town on the hill. 'I am glad,' she said.
'We have come a long way from our
home. I am very tired, and soon our
baby will be born.'

Slowly Joseph led Mary and the
donkey up the hill to the door of the
inn.

'Is there a room for my wife and me?'
Joseph asked the innkeeper.

The innkeeper shook his head. 'Every
room is full,' he said. Then he looked
at Mary and he felt sorry for her. 'I
have a stable,' he said. 'You can stay
there if you like.'

'Yes, please,' Mary said quickly.

So Joseph and Mary and the donkey
went into the stable, and Mary lay
down on the hay.

That night Jesus, the Son of God, was
born in the stable. Mary dressed him
in soft cloth, and put him in a manger.
She felt very happy.

That same night some shepherds were
out on the hills looking after their
sheep. It was a dark night and they sat
close to the fire.

'Look, all of you!' one shepherd
called out suddenly. 'What's that bright
light in the sky?'

They all looked up, and then hid their faces from the light.

'It must be an angel,' said one.

'Don't be afraid,' said the angel. 'I bring you good news. Tonight, in Bethlehem, a baby has been born who is your King. You will know this is true when you see him lying in a manger.'

Then the sky was full of angels singing to God.

When the angels had gone, the shepherds ran up the hill to Bethlehem and found the stable.

The shepherds saw the baby in the manger just as the angel had said, and they were full of joy.

'An angel told us to come,' they said to Mary and Joseph. 'Your baby is God's King. We saw all the angels singing to God.'

Later, as they went slowly back to their sheep, they said to everyone they met, 'Give thanks to God, God's King is born.'

Mary looked after Jesus and she never forgot what the shepherds had said.

Luke 2. 1–20

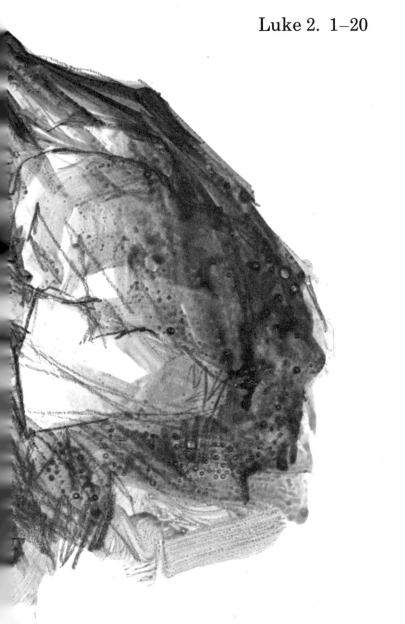

This is my Son

'John the Baptist is by the river again, I am going to see what he does,' said one man to another.

'I'll come with you,' said his friend.

Soon many people were standing round John.

'Stop doing bad things and trust God,' said John. 'Come and be baptized in the river to show that you are sorry for the bad things you have done.'

Many people came to John and he baptized them, taking them down to the water and dipping them in.

One day Jesus came. 'Will you baptize me, John?' he asked.

'You don't need to be baptized,' said John. 'You have done nothing bad.'

'But God wants me to be baptized,' Jesus said.

So John baptized him. As Jesus came up out of the water, God said, 'This is my much loved Son. I am very pleased with him.'

Soon after this, Jesus went to Nazareth. He went into the church and read to all the people from God's book.

This is what he read—

'God has sent me to tell good news to poor people, to make blind people see, and to tell you that God will be good to all who come to him.'

Then Jesus said to everyone, 'Today these words have come true.'

Matthew 3
Luke 4. 31–37

I'll teach you to catch men

'I think Jesus is great,' said Peter, as he was out catching fish with his brother, Andrew. 'I would go anywhere with him.'

'So would I,' said Andrew. 'I would love to be his friend.'

Just then Jesus came walking along by the sea, and saw Peter and Andrew. 'Come with me,' he said, 'and I will teach you to catch men.'

At once they came to Jesus.

Not far away James and John were mending their nets. They were in the boat with their father. Jesus called to them, too, and said, 'Come with me.'

So James and John left their father and followed Jesus.

These four men became Jesus' best
friends and went everywhere with him.

Matthew 4. 18–22

The little girl who was dead

Jairus ran along the road to the Sea of Galilee, looking for Jesus. 'Where is he?' he asked. 'I must find him.'

'Here he comes,' someone said. 'He's on the water, in that boat.'

Jairus ran quickly down to the water, and pushed his way through the crowds. As soon as Jesus got off the boat, Jairus fell down at his feet.

'My little girl is very ill,' he said, 'and no one can make her well. Please will you come to her?'

'I will come at once,' said Jesus. 'Take me to your house.'

As they were on the way, a man came running up to Jairus. 'It's no good,' he said sadly. 'Your little girl is dead.'

Jesus looked at Jairus. 'Don't be afraid,' he said. 'Just trust me and she will be well.'

When they got to the house, there were many people there, and they were all crying. Jesus told them to stay outside and he went in with three of his friends and the little girl's mother and father. The little girl lay very still on her bed. Jesus held her hand. 'Get up, little girl,' he said, softly.

She opened her eyes and looked at him. Then she sat up.

'She will be all right now,' said Jesus to her mother and father. 'Give her something to eat.'

Mark 5. 21–24, 35–43

The boy who gave Jesus his dinner

'Can I go and see Jesus?' a boy asked
his mother one sunny morning. 'He
is up on the hill and crowds of people
are going there.'

'Yes, you can go,' said his mother.
'Jesus is a good man, and he is always
helping people. You will want

something to eat. Take these five little rolls and two fish.'

The boy ran off with his friends and soon came to where Jesus was sitting on a big rock. He pushed past the people until he was close to Jesus. All day he listened to Jesus. He forgot all about his dinner.

Then one of Jesus' friends said, 'It is time the people went home. Send them away so that they can buy food.'

'You feed them,' said Jesus.

'But we have no food,' they said, 'and there are more than five thousand people here.'

'Find out how much food there is,' said Jesus.

The boy ran up to Andrew. 'I have five rolls and two fish,' he said. 'It's not much, but Jesus can have it.'

Andrew took the food to Jesus.

'Tell everyone to sit down,' said Jesus. Then he thanked God for the food and gave it to his friends to pass round. All the people had as much as they could eat.

Afterwards they picked up the bits that were left and there were twelve bags full.

When the people saw what Jesus had done, they said, 'He must be our new king.'

Mark 6. 30–44

The man in a tree

'Where are all these people going?'
asked Zacchaeus.

'They are going to see Jesus,' said
a boy.

Zacchaeus said, 'I want to see Jesus,
too.' So he went with all the people.
But Zacchaeus was a very little man,
and he couldn't see over the people's

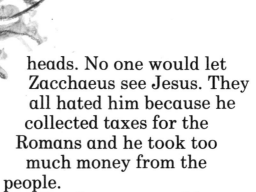

heads. No one would let Zacchaeus see Jesus. They all hated him because he collected taxes for the Romans and he took too much money from the people.

Then Zacchaeus saw a big tree by the road. He ran to it and pulled himself up into the branches. Now he could see very well.

As Jesus walked under the tree he suddenly stopped and looked up. Everyone saw Zacchaeus and made fun of him in the tree. But Jesus said, 'Come down, Zacchaeus, I want to go to your house.'

So Zacchaeus slid down happily and took Jesus home.

Outside the house people were talking about Zacchaeus. 'If Jesus knew how bad Zacchaeus is,' they said, 'he would not go to his house.'

But Jesus did know, and he looked sadly at Zacchaeus. Then Zacchaeus was sorry and he knew that he must stop doing bad things.

He went out to all the people and said, 'If I have taken too much money from any of you, I will give you back four times as much.'

Gladly Jesus said, 'Zacchaeus, today you have become one of God's children.'

Luke 19. 1–10

Here is your King

Crowds of people were going to Jerusalem for a holiday, and Jesus and his friends were going, too.

As they came close to Jerusalem, Jesus said to two of his friends, 'Go to those houses over there, and you will find a donkey's colt. Bring him to me. Tell the man who owns the donkey that I want him.'

The two friends found the donkey just as Jesus had said. As they led the donkey back to Jesus, they were very glad. 'Jesus is going to be King,' they said. 'He is going to ride into Jerusalem just like our kings always used to do.'

One of Jesus' friends put his coat on the donkey for Jesus to sit on.

Then all his friends sang and shouted, 'God bless the King. God bless the King of Israel.'

Many other people were on the road, too. 'It's Jesus,' they called to one another. 'It's Jesus. He's going into Jerusalem just like our kings used to do. Let's cheer him.'

They pulled branches from the trees and waved and sang and cheered.

So Jesus rode down the hill and into Jerusalem.

But the rulers of the Jews were very angry. 'We must stop this,' they said.

Mark 11. 1–10
Luke 19. 28–40

The secret supper

Two men walked quickly along the dark streets of Jerusalem. They were going to have a secret supper with Jesus in a secret room where those who wanted to kill him could not find him.

All Jesus' friends came and sat down at the table. But everyone was thinking, 'Our feet are dusty from the dusty roads. They should be washed before we eat. But who will do it? Not *me*, I'm too good for that job.'

Jesus could tell what they were thinking. So he took some water and he washed everyone's feet.

When he had finished he said, 'You call me Lord, and that is right. I am your King and Lord, and I am willing to do this for you, so you must be willing to do things for one another.'

John 13. 1–17

In the garden

'Let's go into the garden on the hill,' said Jesus after the supper.

When they got there, he said, 'You stay here. I am very sad and I am going to pray. Keep awake and pray, too.'

He went a few steps away and prayed. 'Please, Father,' he said, 'please don't let these things happen. But do let what you want happen, and not what I want.'

When he went back to his friends, they were asleep. 'Wake up,' he said. 'The time has come.'

Suddenly there was the tramp of feet and the crash of sticks, and a gang of men rushed into the garden. They were led by Judas, who was one of Jesus' close friends. Judas kissed Jesus. Then the men said, 'That's him,' and they dragged Jesus off to the ruler's house.

All Jesus' friends ran away.

Mark 14. 32–50

The Roman ruler and Jesus

'Let's take Jesus to Pilate,' said
the rulers of the Jews. 'We
cannot kill Jesus, but if we tell Pilate
that he is a bad man, he will have
him killed.'

So first thing in the morning they
took Jesus to the house of Pilate,
who was the Roman ruler.

'Are you the King of the Jews?'
Pilate asked Jesus.

'So you say,' said Jesus.

Pilate did not think that Jesus was
a bad man. So he asked the Jews
what they had against him.

'He sets the people against the
Romans and tells them not to pay their
taxes,' they said.

'What do you say to this?' Pilate
asked Jesus. 'Is it right?'

But Jesus said nothing.
'I find nothing bad in this man,' said
Pilate. He wanted to let Jesus go.
'I always set one man free at this
holiday time,' he said. 'Shall
it be Jesus or that robber, Barabbas?'

All the people shouted, 'Barabbas!'

'Then what shall I do with Jesus?'
asked Pilate.

'Kill him,' shouted the people.
'Put him on a cross.' Their rulers
had made them say this.

Pilate was afraid of the people. He
wanted to please them. So he said
that Jesus must be killed on a cross.
'But you are doing this, not me,' he
said to the people.

Pilate took some water and washed
his hands. 'I am washing my hands
clean to show that I am not to blame
for Jesus' death,' he said.

Then he sent Jesus to be killed.

Matthew 27. 11–31

On the cross

The Roman soldiers took Jesus to a hill close to Jerusalem, and at nine o'clock in the morning they hung him there on a cross. Over the cross were the words, 'The King of the Jews'.

Two robbers were hung there with him, one on his right-hand side and one on his left.

Many people who came by made fun of him, but Jesus only said, 'Father, forgive them, for they don't know what they are doing.'

One of the robbers made fun of him, too. 'If you are a King,' he said, 'do something to help yourself–and us.'

But the other one said, 'We are here because of the bad things we have done, but this man has done nothing bad.' Then he said to Jesus, 'Lord, think of me when you are King.'

Jesus said, 'Today you shall be with me in my Father's home.'

At midday the sky went black. It was dark everywhere until three o'clock. Then Jesus called out, 'It is finished!' and he died.

When one of the soldiers saw how Jesus died, he said, 'This must be the Son of God.'

Some friends of Jesus took his body into a garden close by, and placed it in a cave there. Then they put a big rock over the opening.

Luke 23. 32–56

He
is not here

First thing on Sunday morning some women came to the garden to put oil on Jesus' dead body.

'Look, the rock has been pushed away!' one lady called out. The women stopped still and looked at the cave.

'Who can have done it?' they asked.

Slowly they came closer and looked into the cave. The body of Jesus was not there!

Then they saw a man dressed in white, sitting where the body had been. 'Don't be afraid,' he said. 'Jesus is not here. He is alive again. Go and tell his friends that he is alive and that he will come to them.'

The women ran away from the garden and found Jesus' friends. They told them what they had seen, but the men shook their heads and said, 'That can't be true.'

But Peter and John ran to the garden to see for themselves, and they found the rock pushed away, just as the women had said. They went into the cave and saw that Jesus was not there.

'It must be true. Jesus is alive again!' said John to himself, and he went back home, feeling very happy.

Matthew 28. 1–10
Mark 16. 1–8
Luke 24. 1–12
John 20. 1–10

He is alive!

Mary was all by herself. She stood close to the cave, crying. 'Jesus was my best friend,' she said. 'Now he is dead, and his body has gone.'

Then suddenly, she looked up and saw a man. Thinking he was the gardener, she said, 'If you have taken his body, Sir, please tell me where he is.'

'Mary,' the man said.

It was Jesus! Mary called out, 'My Lord,' and ran to him, laughing.

'Go to my friends,' said Jesus, 'and tell them that you have seen me.'

So Mary rushed back to all Jesus' friends. Full of joy, she called out, 'I have seen Jesus. Jesus is alive.'

John 20. 11–18

Made and printed in Great Britain by Purnell & Sons Ltd., Paulton.